Angel Small Follows the Star

By Karen Langtree
and Gill McLean

Heaven was having a party
to celebrate the birth of Jesus.
Angels had been dancing for days.

Angel Small
lay on a cloud,
gazing across the deep dark universe.
Stars twinkled like
Christmas tree lights.
He looked down at Earth.

Suddenly, he sat up!
Three men were pointing at him.
"Don't panic!" said a voice.
"They're not looking at you.
They're looking at me."

Angel Small turned to see a splendid star shimmering beside him.

"I'm going to guide them on a journey to find King Jesus. Must go! Cheerio! Need to recharge my *Razzle Dazzle*."

"WOW!" thought Angel Small. "I could help. I know where Jesus was born."

No one noticed him sneaking softly away and taking off into the dawn sky.

Angel Small flew down to the Wise Men,
where three camels were being loaded up for the long journey.
"Hello," he said.
"Go away!"
said the first camel, tossing his mane.
"Shoo!"
said the second camel, flicking his tail.

The third camel said,
"Don't mind my brothers, Hakeem and Akeem.
I'm Kamal."

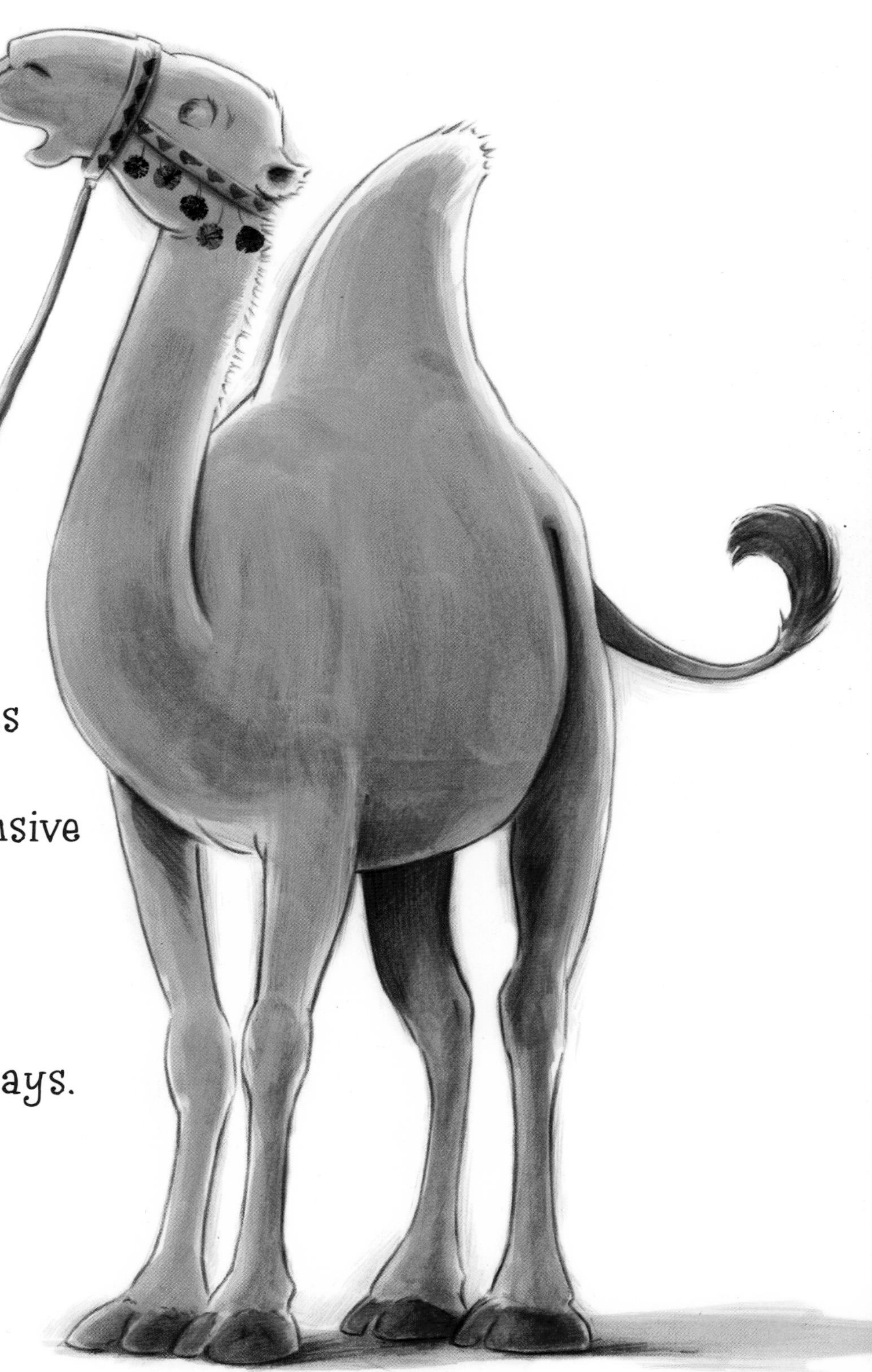

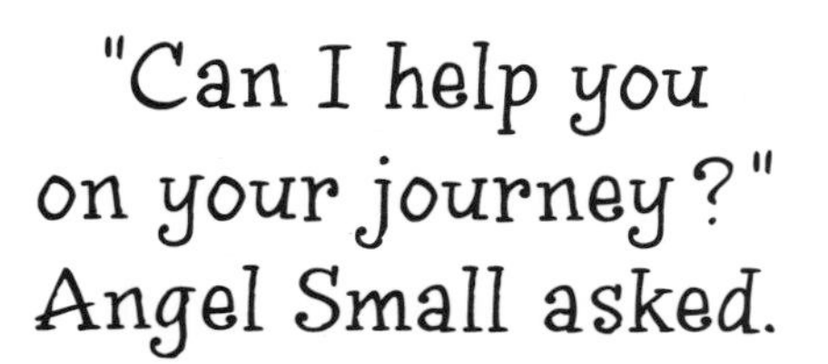

"Can I help you
on your journey?"
Angel Small asked.

The Wise Men wondered what gifts
to take for the new king.
They decided upon the most expensive
ones they could find.

Hakeem and Akeem argued
over who would lead.
Kamal sighed and followed, as always.

The caravan of camels wound its way

along rocky roads and up steep sandy summits.

Diamond stars lit up the night,

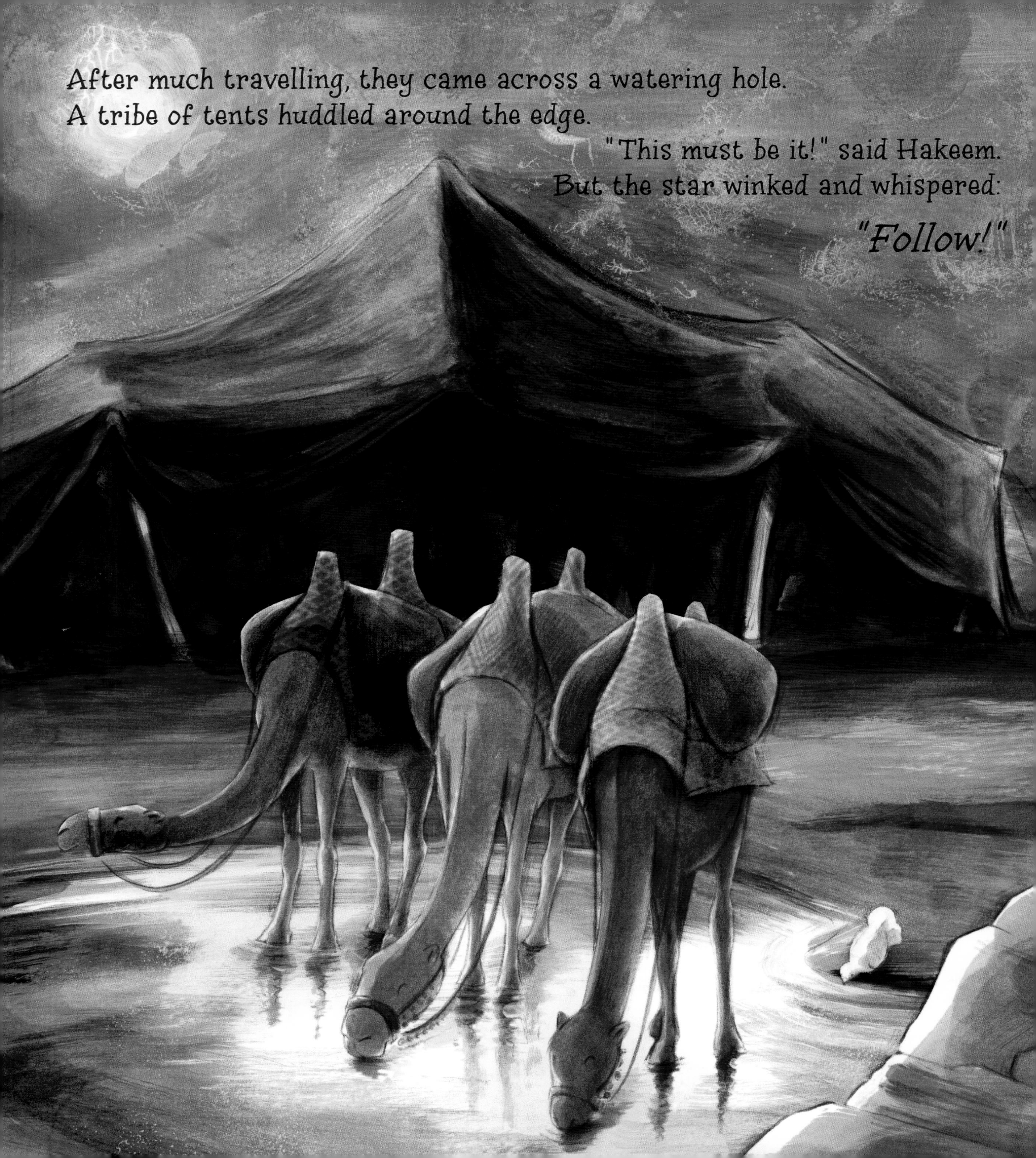

After much travelling, they came across a watering hole.
A tribe of tents huddled around the edge.

"This must be it!" said Hakeem.
But the star winked and whispered:

"Follow!"

A chameleon scampered onto a rock.
Angel Small gasped as a rainbow of rippling colours rolled across his body.

"What are you doing here?" asked the chameleon.

"We're looking for King Jesus," explained Angel Small.

"I'd love to come," sighed the chameleon,
"But I don't have a grand gift."

"Just come as you are," Angel Small said,
"Jesus will *love* your amazing colours.
Hop on board!"

The two troublesome camels pulled the Wise Men in different directions.

"Follow the star!"
Angel Small whispered in Kamal's ear.

Kamal looked up
at the star and said,
"Brothers, *I* think..."
But they were too busy
arguing to listen.

After a long time, they arrived at King Herod's palace.

"This must be it!" said Akeem.

The bright, beautiful star shook her head and sighed.

"Follow!"

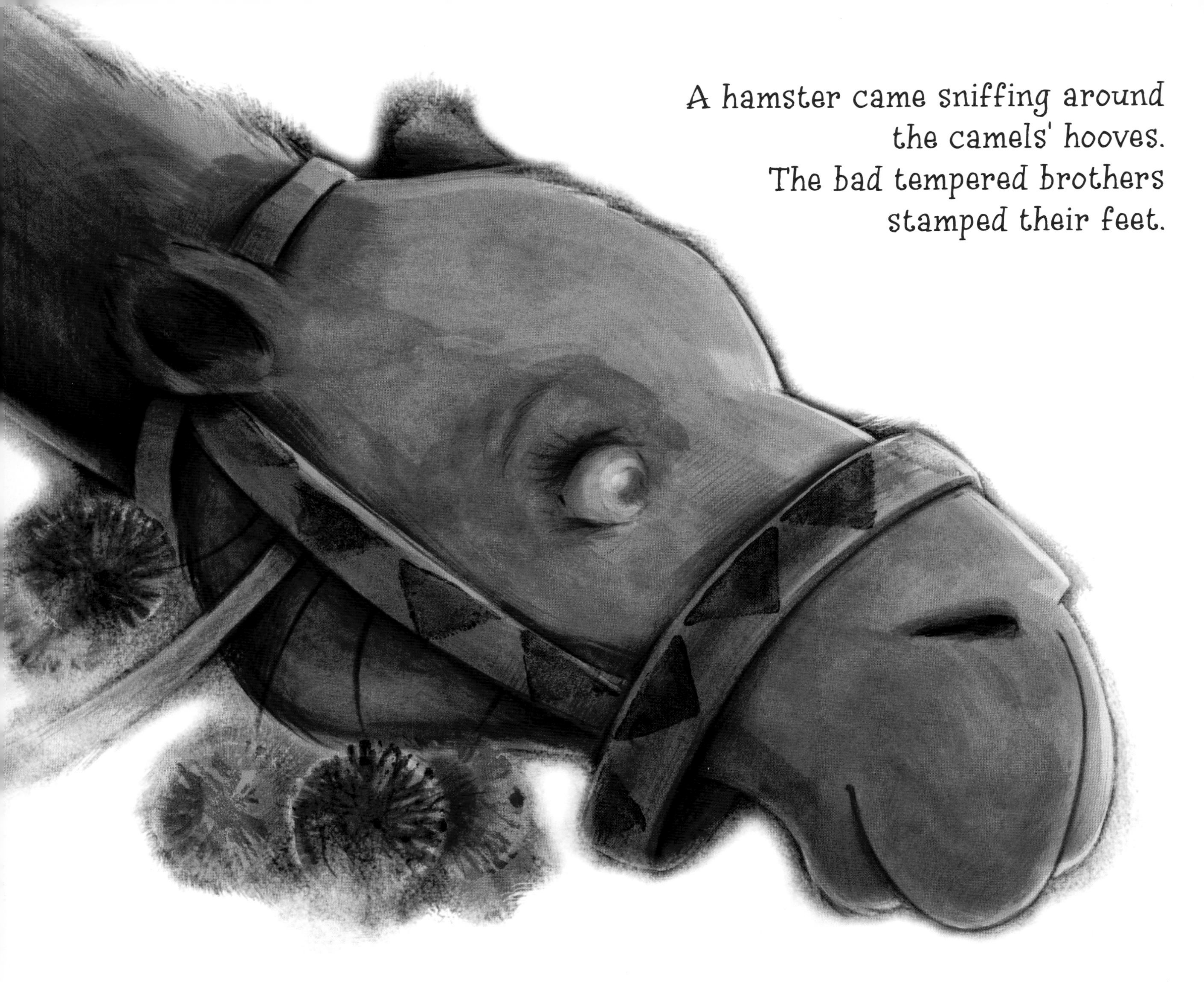

A hamster came sniffing around
the camels' hooves.
The bad tempered brothers
stamped their feet.

"Hello," said Kamal.

"What are you doing here?" asked the hamster.

"We're looking for King Jesus," explained Angel Small.

"I'd love to come," said the hamster, "but my coat's not smart enough."

"Just come as you are," said Angel Small.
"Jesus will *love* your golden, fuzzy fur. Hop on board!"

The bossy brothers jostled for lead position.
"Follow the star!" Angel Small whispered in Kamal's ear.

Kamal looked up to the sky, then boldly strode into the lead.
The star blazed brighter. "Well done, Kamal!"

At last, they approached the little town of Bethlehem.
The star lit up a stable. Kamal stopped.
"*This is it!*" said Angel Small.
"Ridiculous!" cried Hakeem.
"Preposterous!" cried Akeem.

A snowy white dove was resting on the roof.

"We're looking for King Jesus." said Kamal.

"Me too," said the dove, "I've got a gift for him."

She fluttered inside.

The quarrelsome camels
tried to move on,
but Kamal dug in his hooves.

The wise men gave up
and followed the dove
into the stable.

There, lying in a manger, they found the baby king and knew the star had led them to the right place.

They knelt before Jesus and presented their precious gifts.

The baby smiled when he saw
the brightly coloured presents...

...Gold

...Frankincense

...and Myrrh.

"I'm glad you followed the star, Kamal." Angel Small whispered.

"But what present did the dove bring?" asked Kamal.

The little angel smiled and looked up.
The dove was sitting in the rafters.

"I give *myself*," she said.

"Coo - coo!"
Sang the dove
and baby Jesus
drifted off
to sleep.

The story begins...

Do you need a

CHRISTMAS MUSICAL

Have you heard about

Perfect for nativity plays...
Based on the books by
Karen Langtree and **Gill McLean**
with the companion title
Follows the Star

This musical is a delightful adaptation of the Angel Small storybooks. It is just right for Key Stage One to perform (children aged 5 to 7) with short speaking parts and numerous narrators. It can also be adapted to give parts to older children to suit the needs of your school or organisation. The songs are endearing, fun and easy-to-learn.

All available for **instant download** :

- *Playscript*
- *Lead piano score and guitar chords*
- *Backing tracks (with and without vocals)*
- *PowerPoint lyrics for easy learning in the classroom*
- *Background scenery to project behind the action on stage*
- *Free 'Angel Small' picture book*

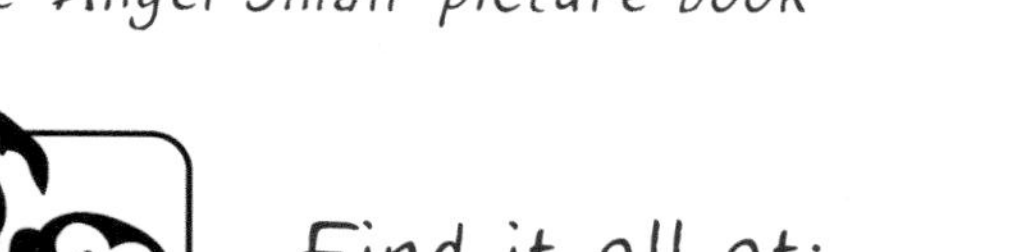

Find it all at:
www.monkeyislandpublishing.com